THE BLUMENFELD ORAL READING A

Included in your test are fi ve (5) sets of Marking copies for the pre-test version and five (5) sets of Marking copies for the after-test (Version B).
This allows you to administer the test up to five times with five different people. Since Samuel L. Blumenfeld, under his copyright protection, does not allow copies of any parts of the test to be reproduced (on a copy machine, etc.), you are being provided with the necessary marking copies for both the pre and after testing up to five times.
The Reading Test ("A" or "B") for the student can be used as many times as you wish, both for the pre-test and the after-test, because it is not marked upon in the process.
If you use up all five sets of Marking copies for either test, and need more, please contact us and we will provide extra copies of either Marking copy for the price of $1.00 each including postage. To obtain extra copies write or call:

The Paradigm Company, 3500 Mountain View Dr. Boise, ID 83704 • (208) 322-4440

ISBN: 0-941995-37-2

Published and distributed by:
The Paradigm Company
3500 Mountain View Drive
Boise, Idaho 83704
(208) 322-4440
Email: alphaphonics@hotmail.com

Books on reading by Samuel L. Blumenfeld:

THE NEW ILLITERATES
HOW TO TUTOR
ALPHA-PHONICS: A PRIMER FOR BEGINNING READERS

For complete information on educational materials by Samuel L. Blumenfeld:

See his comprehensive internet website: www.alphaphonics.com

THE BLUMENFELD ORAL READING ASSESSMENT TEST

The purpose of the Blumenfeld Oral Reading Assessment Test (BORAT) is to permit the tester to determine the student's ability to read. By reading, we mean the ability to translate our alphabetic written language into its precise spoken equivalent.

The four-page test consists of 38 columns of words, each column consisting of 10 words (380 words in all), arranged in a sequence progressing from the simplest three-letter, one syllable words to complex, multisyllabic words.

The first 23 columns test the student's knowledge of the English alphabetic system in its entire range of vowel and consonant spelling forms. This knowledge is generally known as "basic decoding skills."

Columns 24, 25, 27 and 28 test reading ability with a variety of two-syllable words. Columns 26, 29 and 30 consist of three-syllable words. Column 31 consists of common multisyllabic words used in and out of school.

Columns 32-36 consist of more difficult multisyllabic words generally found in such adult-level reading matter as the *Reader's Digest.* Columns 37 and 38 consist of multisyllabic words culled from employment display ads in the *Sunday Boston Globe.*

This is an oral test and therefore does not test comprehension. It tests decoding skills in order to establish whether or not the student can read written English with accuracy. Indeed, many students with good phonetic knowledge may have difficulty with some of the multisyllabic words, indicating a weakness in vocabulary development.

Before administering the test, the tester should read all of the words to make sure that he or she knows their correct pronunciation. An audio tape is available which gives the correct pronunciation of all the words. The tape can be ordered from the Paradigm Company. If the tester is unsure of only a few words, a dictionary will usually provide the correct pronunciation and accentuation. It is important for the tester to know the correct pronunciation of all the words, for wrong accentuation is considered an error.

This test packet contains at least two copies of the test — one for the student to read, and a marking copy for the tester. Each student requires a marking copy as his or her own record of the test. The tester should have as many marking copies as the number of students to be tested. If an entire student body in a school is to be tested, then several hundred marking copies will be needed. If you are a private tutor, keep a stock of marking copies on hand.

The Blumenfeld Oral Reading Assessment Test is copyrighted, and therefore additional copies of the test must be obtained through the Paradigm Company. Please do not copy the test on a copier machine as this would be a breach of the copyright law. As you know, the purpose of copyright is to protect literary property from unauthorized use or publication. Without such protection, authors and publishers would be unable to subsist.

This test packet contains a grade-level scoring chart, and a section on how to interpret the score. Also, at the end of the test are several questions the tester should ask the student. If the student plans to attend college, or pursue a career goal that requires good reading skills, but has tested poorly, an intensive remedial program should be recommended. A knowledge of the schools the student has attended may provide the teacher with information on how the student was taught to read in the primary grades.

Testing Instructions

This test can be given to anyone — from a third-grader to an adult. It is particularly useful in determining the reading skill of adult functional illiterates. First and second graders can be tested by using the first 23 columns only. They will inform the tester on how well the child is mastering the English alphabetic system.

Because this is an oral test, it can only be given to one person at a time. It should be given privately in a room or office where others cannot hear or interrupt. If the test is given at home, a kitchen or dining room table and two chairs would provide a comfortable setting. The student and tester should be close enough so that the tester can hear the student without any difficulty and the student can read in a normal speaking voice.

First, the student fills out the information at the top of the tester's marking copy. When completed, the student hands the marking copy to the tester. The tester then gives the student the reading copy and instructs the student to read the words down each column in regular sequence when told to begin. The student should be told to read for accuracy, not for speed, and to pronounce each word clearly and distinctly.

When the student begins reading, the tester listens carefully, following the words as they are read, putting a check mark only next to those words read incorrectly. Any deviation from the correct pronunciation of the word must be marked as an error. However, if the student first mispronounces a word or misreads it but immediately corrects himself, this should not be marked as an error. If you've already made a check mark, simply put a slash through the check to indicate an immediate self-correction. Under no circumstance should the tester in any way assist the student in reading a word.

Typical errors include gross misreadings, wrong vowel pronunication, wrong accentuation, inability to read the word at all, wrong guessing.

When the student has completed reading all the columns, the tester should add up the check marks in each column and tabulate the total number of errors. The total number of errors is the final score. Check the score against the grade-level chart to arrive at the student's grade-level reading ability.

Interpreting the Score

The lower the score, the better the reader. The higher the score, the poorer the reader. The discrepancy between the student's score and the expected grade-level score will indicate how far behind the student is. For example, if the student is a seventh grader, with an expected score of 45 to 54, who actually scored 100 errors, he or she would have the reading ability of a fourth-grader.

Most important to note is where the errors were made. If the student misread many words in the first 23 columns, then that student has a serious lack of basic phonetic knowledge and is primarily a sight reader. If the student did well on the first 23 columns but then began to falter with the multisyllabic words, then this student has simply not had enough challenging, vocabulary-rich reading in school or at home.

Good readers score at their grade level or better. If you are testing an entire school, you may find one or more third-graders reading at a seventh-grade level, a ninth-grader reading at a third-grade level, and a few twelfth-graders reading at a fifth-grade level. By giving the test to everyone, the administrator will be able to draw a literacy profile of the entire school, thus identifying those who need remedial help. If the entire school tests poorly, then the reading instruction in that school will most likely be at fault.

If you are operating a good private school with good reading instruction but have among your students poor readers from the public schools, this test will help you identify them so that you can offer them remedial or tutorial instruction. In fact, this is an excellent test to administer to students who are applying for admission. In ten minutes this test will provide you with a clear profile of the student's reading skill and his or her ability to handle your school's curriculum. By informing the parent beforehand that the student will need extra tutorial instruction, the additional cost can be factored into the tuition.

If an adult has made many errors in the first 23 columns, then that adult will need an intensive, systematic phonics instruction program, such as *Alpha-Phonics*, to improve his or her reading ability. That individual may have been labeled functionally illiterate or dyslexic. The cure for dyslexia is to become a phonetic reader, and that means instruction in intensive, systematic phonics.

Grade Chart

The following chart is a guide to grade-level reading ability based on the number of errors made by the student in the test:

Grade	Score Parameters
3	110-130
4	95-109
5	75-94
6	55-74
7	45-54
8	40-44
9	35-39
10	30-34
11	25-29
12	20-24

How was this grade chart prepared? In September 1983 this test was given to 207 students in grades 3 through 12 in a private school in Boston. The results made it possible to set parameters of reading ability on the basis of errors made by the students. By averaging the scores of the students in each grade, a mean score was arrived at for the grade permitting the setting of expected or ideal score parameters for each grade.

In actuality, the average scores of each grade were at variance with the expected or ideal scores. Some grades scored at, above, or below the expected average. In the chart below are the actual scores of the students by grade.

Note the amount of information that one was able to gather by the testing. Beginning with the

Grade	Number of Pupils	Average Errors Scored	Expected Grade-level Scores	Errors Scored by Best Reader	Errors Scored by Poorest Reader
3	11	119	110-130	51	230
4	7	105	95-109	39	227
5	0		75-94		
6	21	62	55-74	31	103
7	17	49	45-54	16	83
8	33	48	40-44	12	123
9	42	50	35-39	15	130
10	29	36	30-34	6	111
11	25	29	25-29	8	93
12	22	31	20-24	9	85

seventh grade, the best readers scored far above the twelfth-grade level, while the poorest readers never made it above a fifth-grade level. In addition, the chart reveals that grades 3, 4, 6, 7 and 11 achieved grade-level reading scores but that grades 8, 9, 10 and 12 scored below their expected level. The reason why the ninth-graders did so poorly is because they included many recent arrivals from the public schools with poor reading ability.

Note that the best reader in the third grade scored at the seventh-grade level and that the poorest reader in the twelfth grade scored at a fifth-grade level. The best reader in the school was a 10th grader who made only 6 errors in the test. The poorest reader was a 9th grader who scored at the 3rd-grade level.

Obviously, the scores identfied those students who were in greatest need of help. It was discovered, for example, that 22 students in grades 8 through 12 were reading 4 or more grades below their expected reading level. Two students were reading seven grades below their expected reading level.

Of the 207 students tested in grades 3-12, 106 students (51%) scored at or above their expected grade level, while 101 students (49%) scored below their expected grade level. It was discovered that 42 students scored 3 or more grades below their expected grade level, indicating that a tutorial program was needed to bring these students up to their grade level in reading.

Drawing A School Profile

By administering this test to an entire school, it is possible to gather the following important information:

1. The reading ability of teach student.
2. A determination of how many students are phonetic readers and how many are "sight" readers.
3. The identification of those students who need help.
4. A comparison between those students who were taught to read at the school and those who were taught elsewhere.
5. A literacy profile of each class — identifying the best reader and the poorest.
6. Matching a student's reading ability with his or her career goal.
7. An evaluation of the school's overall language arts program.
8. An evaluation of the school's beginning reading program.
9. A comparison between schools that have administered the same test.
10. Data that will permit the school to determine why some students are superior readers and others very poor readers. Are the differences attributable to beginning reading instruction or other factors? Finding out where and how these students were taught to read in the first three grades would provide very valuable information about different reading instruction programs.

Follow Up Testing

The Paradigm Company publishes the Blumenfeld Oral Reading Assessment Test in two versions (A & B) so that students can be retested at a later date after tutorial or remedial help. The format of the test is the same, but the words are different, thereby permitting the tester to measure progress made by the student.

Evaluating Home Schoolers

The BORAT provides home-schooling parents with a very easy and quick means of evaluating their children's reading ability. These evaluations will be useful later should the family decide to place the child in a school or when the student applies for college entrance.

Consultation Services

The Paradigm Company provides in-service consultation for schools wishing to administer the test to the student body. For fees and availability or for additional copies of the test please write *The Paradigm Company, 3500 Mountain View Drive., Boise, Idaho 83704*

THE BLUMENFELD ORAL READING ASSESSMENT TEST

Reading Copy (Version A)

1	2	3	4	5	6	7
mad	dad	make	leak	time	joke	tune
yen	vex	paid	yield	like	boat	fuse
bit	dim	wait	she	sight	soap	huge
hog	fog	game	dream	size	row	crude
mum	cub	eight	weep	fire	cold	new
nap	jam	say	seat	cry	nose	blue
let	yet	jail	mean	dice	hope	chew
rib	fig	cage	treat	shy	phone	juice
top	cop	weigh	seed	high	slow	zoo
dug	gut	fade	brief	price	dome	spoon

8	9	10	11	12	13	14
food	out	Joyce	car	ball	serve	fam
wood	now	toy	sharp	yawn	term	hap
should	house	boil	spark	fault	girl	dex
pool	count	coin	charm	raw	shirt	seg
too	brown	void	chart	cause	thirst	dib
room	ounce	boy	charge	talk	nurse	min
book	ground	moist	farce	haunt	earn	jod
could	crowd	Troy	card	crawl	earth	nov
crook	owl	foil	large	call	worm	lub
nook	our	join	arch	caught	burn	sut

THE BLUMENFELD ORAL READING ASSESSMENT TEST

15	16	17	18	19	20
blunt	slump	trust	able	who	this
brash	shrimp	thrash	fiddle	eye	which
clamp	smash	twitch	cattle	your	chap
crutch	snarl	preach	struggle	where	sheath
dredge	sprang	threat	single	young	while
dwell	stomp	streak	fumble	pull	church
flush	strand	text	stifle	door	rash
frost	swift	kept	wriggle	enough	those
grudge	scalp	brisk	strangle	sew	when
prompt	scrunch	draft	turtle	touch	ash

21	22	23	24	25	26
nation	scheme	Philip	napkin	promptly	national
action	chorus	phony	gallon	begrudge	consumption
patient	chemist	phrase	chapel	slothful	imagine
mission	school	physics	kidnap	tactless	tyranny
special	Christmas	graphic	vivid	luncheon	possible
capture	psychic	photo	pencil	witchcraft	difference
question	myth	rough	mimic	chopstick	judicious
fusion	system	cough	vanish	swiftly	represent
leisure	syntax	laugh	cactus	cascade	incident
tissue	syrup	draught	signal	spaceship	consonant

THE BLUMENFELD ORAL READING ASSESSMENT TEST

27	28	29	30	31
concern	chastened	artisan	eccentric	manager
routine	contrite	subsidies	applicants	information
asphalt	realty	upheavals	excesses	registration
prepare	apprised	ascertain	epithets	biographical
nasal	derived	resilience	exultant	photogenic
assigned	pattern	prodigious	contrary	discovery
rely	inane	equity	imminent	immediately
triumph	regime	potentate	fortified	supervision
bestow	novice	lunacy	conveyor	vacation
technique	precepts	antidote	decisive	environment

32	33	34	35
interrogation	diminutive	irresponsible	indignation
concentrated	spontaneous	surreptitiously	undemocratically
inconceivable	tremendously	representative	customarily
collaboration	emulation	consanguinity	idiosyncracies
accomplices	apostrophe	justifiable	indistinguishable
deregulation	revolution	totalitarian	intimidated
reapportionment	enunciate	infallibility	entrepreneur
contemptuous	conscientious	analytical	simultaneously
incompatibility	dictatorship	climatology	interminable
formidable	combustible	anonymity	meticulously

THE BLUMENFELD ORAL READING ASSESSMENT TEST

36	37	38
illumination	candidate	microprocessor
unimaginable	productivity	facilities
replicated	exceptional	confidential
reverberating	pneumatic	multidisciplinary
ludicrously	semiconductor	neurosurgery
computerized	collateral	coordinator
contiguous	appropriate	prototypes
ephemeral	responsibilities	negotiations
resuscitated	manufacturing	synonymous
anesthesiologist	innovation	installation

The Blumenfeld Oral Reading Assessment Test
Reading Copy (Version B)

1	2	3	4	5	6	7
fad	dab	bake	peak	dime	poke	dune
yet	wax	maid	shield	bike	coat	muse
lit	did	gait	we	light	soar	huge
bog	gut	tame	cream	prize	crow	rude
sum	cup	weight	seep	hire	fold	few
pan	jet	day	bleat	fry	pose	true
met	yam	fail	clean	nice	rope	shrew
dim	fog	page	feat	sty	moan	sluice
hop	cob	vein	deed	thigh	grow	goof
mug	gut	wade	chief	thrice	home	croon

8	9	10	11	12	13	14
mood	pout	Royce	far	call	nerve	maf
hood	how	coy	harp	dawn	germ	hab
would	douse	foil	stark	fault	girl	yex
cool	mount	loin	shard	clause	burst	beb
shook	crown	voice	carp	jaw	flirt	teg
broom	bounce	joy	charge	balk	purse	hin
cook	found	foist	farce	daunt	learn	jub
could	crowd	ploy	lard	crawl	earth	niv
zoom	fowl	coil	barge	fall	worth	lut
hook	hour	toy	arch	fraught	turn	suz

The Blumenfeld Oral Reading Assessment Test
(Version B)

15	16	17	18	19	20
blast	slump	thrust	fable	whom	thin
brush	swamp	brash	riddle	eye	which
clump	stash	twitch	bottle	your	champ
crash	snarl	breach	straggle	were	shield
drudge	spring	sweat	mingle	youngster	whilst
dwarf	stump	strength	stumble	bull	church
flash	string	next	trifle	floors	dash
front	shrift	crept	wriggle	enough	these
graft	scalp	brusk	wrangle	two	what
prompt	scrounge	craft	hurtle	only	fresh

21	22	23	24	25	26
station	schedule	Phyllis	tidbit	spendthrift	sensation
faction	choral	phone	ribbon	slingshot	assumption
patience	chemical	phase	tablet	crankcase	imagine
fission	scholar	physical	picnic	dustpan	despotic
racial	Christian	graphite	civil	flagpoles	probable
rapture	psychotic	phosphate	within	crispness	diffident
bastion	mythical	tough	liquid	grandstand	dominion
pleasure	symphony	cough	blemish	spotless	resentment
lesion	systemic	laughter	mascot	hamstring	commodity
issue	character	draught	lentil	platelet	accident

The Blumenfeld Oral Reading Assessment Test
(Version B)

27	28	29	30	31
preserve	hastened	partisan	nemesis	principal
berserk	epoch	rapsodies	reprisal	semester
censure	fledgling	magnesia	skeptical	scholastic
asthma	grenade	novella	hypoderm	historical
diffuse	deprived	reprobate	gardenia	vaccinations
resigned	inscribe	hydrofoil	aqueduct	autobiographical
defy	demure	demagogue	asterisk	counselor
chromic	maestro	permeate	eminent	supervisory
betroth	limelight	placebo	bivouac	ecological
physique	mortgage	thoroughfare	coercive	valedictorian

32	33	34	35
interrogatory	femininity	unalienable	pathogenesis
concentration	gentility	reconnaissance	confiscatory
coincidental	guarantee	septuagenarian	stereotypical
dialectic	heterogeneous	stratagem	idiosyncratic
appropriate	ideogram	hierarchy	premeditated
asinine	inscrutable	espionage	pseudonym
craniology	modification	inviolability	rigmarole
denationalize	obsolescence	ludicrous	knavery
epileptic	pistachio	noncarnivorous	hypocritically
facetious	polytheism	obstetrician	quiescent

The Blumenfeld Oral Reading Assessment Test

36	37	38
hypochondriac	sophistication	radioactivity
impermeable	ministerial	simulator
diversionary	elegiac	privatization
matriculate	gregarious	statistician
mercenary	pneumonia	tautology
onomatopoeia	lobotomy	ventriloquy
lithography	immunology	topographer
perfunctory	libertarianism	mistletoe
quintessential	rejuvenation	individualize
schizophrenic	malfeasance	extraterrestrial

THE BLUMENFELD ORAL READING ASSESSMENT TEST

Marking Copy (Version A)

Name			Age	Grade	Date	
1	2	3	4	5	6	7
mad	dad	make	leak	time	joke	tune
yen	vex	paid	yield	like	boat	fuse
bit	dim	wait	she	sight	soap	huge
hog	fog	game	dream	size	row	crude
mum	cub	eight	weep	fire	cold	new
nap	jam	say	seat	cry	nose	blue
let	yet	jail	mean	dice	hope	chew
rib	fig	cage	treat	shy	phone	juice
top	cop	weigh	seed	high	slow	zoo
dug	gut	fade	brief	price	dome	spoon

8	9	10	11	12	13	14
food	out	Joyce	car	ball	serve	fam
wood	now	toy	sharp	yawn	term	hap
should	house	boil	spark	fault	girl	dex
pool	count	coin	charm	raw	shirt	seg
too	brown	void	chart	cause	thirst	dib
room	ounce	boy	charge	talk	nurse	min
book	ground	moist	farce	haunt	earn	jod
could	crowd	Troy	card	crawl	earth	nov
crook	owl	foil	large	call	worm	lub
nook	our	join	arch	caught	burn	sut

THE BLUMENFELD ORAL READING ASSESSMENT TEST

15	16	17	18	19	20
blunt	slump	trust	able	who	this
brash	shrimp	thrash	fiddle	eye	which
clamp	smash	twitch	cattle	your	chap
crutch	snarl	preach	struggle	where	sheath
dredge	sprang	threat	single	young	while
dwell	stomp	streak	fumble	pull	church
flush	strand	text	stifle	door	rash
frost	swift	kept	wriggle	enough	those
grudge	scalp	brisk	strangle	sew	when
prompt	scrunch	draft	turtle	touch	ash

21	22	23	24	25	26
nation	scheme	Philip	napkin	promptly	national
action	chorus	phony	gallon	begrudge	consumption
patient	chemist	phrase	chapel	slothful	imagine
mission	school	physics	kidnap	tactless	tyranny
special	Christmas	graphic	vivid	luncheon	possible
capture	psychic	photo	pencil	witchcraft	difference
question	myth	rough	mimic	chopstick	judicious
fusion	system	cough	vanish	swiftly	represent
leisure	syntax	laugh	cactus	cascade	incident
tissue	syrup	draught	signal	spaceship	consonant

THE BLUMENFELD ORAL READING ASSESSMENT TEST

27	28	29	30	31
concern	chastened	artisan	eccentric	manager
routine	contrite	subsidies	applicants	information
asphalt	realty	upheavals	excesses	registration
prepare	apprised	ascertain	epithets	biographical
nasal	derived	resilience	exultant	photogenic
assigned	pattern	prodigious	contrary	discovery
rely	inane	equity	imminent	immediately
triumph	regime	potentate	fortified	supervision
bestow	novice	lunacy	conveyor	vacation
technique	precepts	antidote	decisive	environment

32	33	34	35
interrogation	diminutive	irresponsible	indignation
concentrated	spontaneous	surreptitiously	undemocratically
inconceivable	tremendously	representative	customarily
collaboration	emulation	consanguinity	idiosyncracies
accomplices	apostrophe	justifiable	indistinguishable
deregulation	revolution	totalitarian	intimidated
reapportionment	enunciate	infallibility	entrepreneur
contemptuous	conscientious	analytical	simultaneously
incompatibility	dictatorship	climatology	interminable
formidable	combustible	anonymity	meticulously

THE BLUMENFELD ORAL READING ASSESSMENT TEST

36	37	38
illumination	candidate	microprocessor
unimaginable	productivity	facilities
replicated	exceptional	confidential
reverberating	pneumatic	multidisciplinary
ludicrously	semiconductor	neurosurgery
computerized	collateral	coordinator
contiguous	appropriate	prototypes
ephemeral	responsibilities	negotiations
resuscitated	manufacturing	synonymous
anesthesiologist	innovation	installation

Score (Number of errors by column)

1___	11___	21___	31___
2___	12___	22___	32___
3___	13___	23___	33___
4___	14___	24___	34___
5___	15___	25___	35___
6___	16___	26___	36___
7___	17___	27___	37___
8___	18___	28___	38___
9___	19___	29___	
10__	20___	30___	Total___

Final Score_____ Reading Grade Level _____

Do you plan to attend a college? _____

What is your career goal?_____

What schools have you attended?_____

THE BLUMENFELD ORAL READING ASSESSMENT TEST

Marking Copy (Version A)

Name			Age	Grade	Date	

1	2	3	4	5	6	7
mad	dad	make	leak	time	joke	tune
yen	vex	paid	yield	like	boat	fuse
bit	dim	wait	she	sight	soap	huge
hog	fog	game	dream	size	row	crude
mum	cub	eight	weep	fire	cold	new
nap	jam	say	seat	cry	nose	blue
let	yet	jail	mean	dice	hope	chew
rib	fig	cage	treat	shy	phone	juice
top	cop	weigh	seed	high	slow	zoo
dug	gut	fade	brief	price	dome	spoon

8	9	10	11	12	13	14
food	out	Joyce	car	ball	serve	fam
wood	now	toy	sharp	yawn	term	hap
should	house	boil	spark	fault	girl	dex
pool	count	coin	charm	raw	shirt	seg
too	brown	void	chart	cause	thirst	dib
room	ounce	boy	charge	talk	nurse	min
book	ground	moist	farce	haunt	earn	jod
could	crowd	Troy	card	crawl	earth	nov
crook	owl	foil	large	call	worm	lub
nook	our	join	arch	caught	burn	sut

NOTE: Teacher may wish to remove for ease of scoring

© 1991 Samuel L. Blumenfeld

THE BLUMENFELD ORAL READING ASSESSMENT TEST

15	16	17	18	19	20
blunt	slump	trust	able	who	this
brash	shrimp	thrash	fiddle	eye	which
clamp	smash	twitch	cattle	your	chap
crutch	snarl	preach	struggle	where	sheath
dredge	sprang	threat	single	young	while
dwell	stomp	streak	fumble	pull	church
flush	strand	text	stifle	door	rash
frost	swift	kept	wriggle	enough	those
grudge	scalp	brisk	strangle	sew	when
prompt	scrunch	draft	turtle	touch	ash

21	22	23	24	25	26
nation	scheme	Philip	napkin	promptly	national
action	chorus	phony	gallon	begrudge	consumption
patient	chemist	phrase	chapel	slothful	imagine
mission	school	physics	kidnap	tactless	tyranny
special	Christmas	graphic	vivid	luncheon	possible
capture	psychic	photo	pencil	witchcraft	difference
question	myth	rough	mimic	chopstick	judicious
fusion	system	cough	vanish	swiftly	represent
leisure	syntax	laugh	cactus	cascade	incident
tissue	syrup	draught	signal	spaceship	consonant

THE BLUMENFELD ORAL READING ASSESSMENT TEST

27	28	29	30	31
concern	chastened	artisan	eccentric	manager
routine	contrite	subsidies	applicants	information
asphalt	realty	upheavals	excesses	registration
prepare	apprised	ascertain	epithets	biographical
nasal	derived	resilience	exultant	photogenic
assigned	pattern	prodigious	contrary	discovery
rely	inane	equity	imminent	immediately
triumph	regime	potentate	fortified	supervision
bestow	novice	lunacy	conveyor	vacation
technique	precepts	antidote	decisive	environment

32	33	34	35
interrogation	diminutive	irresponsible	indignation
concentrated	spontaneous	surreptitiously	undemocratically
inconceivable	tremendously	representative	customarily
collaboration	emulation	consanguinity	idiosyncracies
accomplices	apostrophe	justifiable	indistinguishable
deregulation	revolution	totalitarian	intimidated
reapportionment	enunciate	infallibility	entrepreneur
contemptuous	conscientious	analytical	simultaneously
incompatibility	dictatorship	climatology	interminable
formidable	combustible	anonymity	meticulously

THE BLUMENFELD ORAL READING ASSESSMENT TEST

36	37	38
illumination	candidate	microprocessor
unimaginable	productivity	facilities
replicated	exceptional	confidential
reverberating	pneumatic	multidisciplinary
ludicrously	semiconductor	neurosurgery
computerized	collateral	coordinator
contiguous	appropriate	prototypes
ephemeral	responsibilities	negotiations
resuscitated	manufacturing	synonymous
anesthesiologist	innovation	installation

Score (Number of errors by column)

1___	11___	21___	31___
2___	12___	22___	32___
3___	13___	23___	33___
4___	14___	24___	34___
5___	15___	25___	35___
6___	16___	26___	36___
7___	17___	27___	37___
8___	18___	28___	38___
9___	19___	29___	
10___	20___	30___	Total___

Final Score_____ **Reading Grade Level** _____

Do you plan to attend a college? _____

What is your career goal?_____

What schools have you attended?_____

THE BLUMENFELD ORAL READING ASSESSMENT TEST

Marking Copy (Version A)

Name			Age	Grade	Date	

1	2	3	4	5	6	7
mad	dad	make	leak	time	joke	tune
yen	vex	paid	yield	like	boat	fuse
bit	dim	wait	she	sight	soap	huge
hog	fog	game	dream	size	row	crude
mum	cub	eight	weep	fire	cold	new
nap	jam	say	seat	cry	nose	blue
let	yet	jail	mean	dice	hope	chew
rib	fig	cage	treat	shy	phone	juice
top	cop	weigh	seed	high	slow	zoo
dug	gut	fade	brief	price	dome	spoon

8	9	10	11	12	13	14
food	out	Joyce	car	ball	serve	fam
wood	now	toy	sharp	yawn	term	hap
should	house	boil	spark	fault	girl	dex
pool	count	coin	charm	raw	shirt	seg
too	brown	void	chart	cause	thirst	dib
room	ounce	boy	charge	talk	nurse	min
book	ground	moist	farce	haunt	earn	jod
could	crowd	Troy	card	crawl	earth	nov
crook	owl	foil	large	call	worm	lub
nook	our	join	arch	caught	burn	sut

NOTE: Teacher may wish to remove for ease of scoring

THE BLUMENFELD ORAL READING ASSESSMENT TEST

15	16	17	18	19	20
blunt	slump	trust	able	who	this
brash	shrimp	thrash	fiddle	eye	which
clamp	smash	twitch	cattle	your	chap
crutch	snarl	preach	struggle	where	sheath
dredge	sprang	threat	single	young	while
dwell	stomp	streak	fumble	pull	church
flush	strand	text	stifle	door	rash
frost	swift	kept	wriggle	enough	those
grudge	scalp	brisk	strangle	sew	when
prompt	scrunch	draft	turtle	touch	ash

21	22	23	24	25	26
nation	scheme	Philip	napkin	promptly	national
action	chorus	phony	gallon	begrudge	consumption
patient	chemist	phrase	chapel	slothful	imagine
mission	school	physics	kidnap	tactless	tyranny
special	Christmas	graphic	vivid	luncheon	possible
capture	psychic	photo	pencil	witchcraft	difference
question	myth	rough	mimic	chopstick	judicious
fusion	system	cough	vanish	swiftly	represent
leisure	syntax	laugh	cactus	cascade	incident
tissue	syrup	draught	signal	spaceship	consonant

THE BLUMENFELD ORAL READING ASSESSMENT TEST

27	28	29	30	31
concern	chastened	artisan	eccentric	manager
routine	contrite	subsidies	applicants	information
asphalt	realty	upheavals	excesses	registration
prepare	apprised	ascertain	epithets	biographical
nasal	derived	resilience	exultant	photogenic
assigned	pattern	prodigious	contrary	discovery
rely	inane	equity	imminent	immediately
triumph	regime	potentate	fortified	supervision
bestow	novice	lunacy	conveyor	vacation
technique	precepts	antidote	decisive	environment

32	33	34	35
interrogation	diminutive	irresponsible	indignation
concentrated	spontaneous	surreptitiously	undemocratically
inconceivable	tremendously	representative	customarily
collaboration	emulation	consanguinity	idiosyncracies
accomplices	apostrophe	justifiable	indistinguishable
deregulation	revolution	totalitarian	intimidated
reapportionment	enunciate	infallibility	entrepreneur
contemptuous	conscientious	analytical	simultaneously
incompatibility	dictatorship	climatology	interminable
formidable	combustible	anonymity	meticulously

THE BLUMENFELD ORAL READING ASSESSMENT TEST

36	37	38
illumination	candidate	microprocessor
unimaginable	productivity	facilities
replicated	exceptional	confidential
reverberating	pneumatic	multidisciplinary
ludicrously	semiconductor	neurosurgery
computerized	collateral	coordinator
contiguous	appropriate	prototypes
ephemeral	responsibilities	negotiations
resuscitated	manufacturing	synonymous
anesthesiologist	innovation	installation

Score (Number of errors by column)

1___	11___	21___	31___
2___	12___	22___	32___
3___	13___	23___	33___
4___	14___	24___	34___
5___	15___	25___	35___
6___	16___	26___	36___
7___	17___	27___	37___
8___	18___	28___	38___
9___	19___	29___	
10___	20___	30___	Total___

Final Score_____ Reading Grade Level _____

Do you plan to attend a college? _____

What is your career goal?_____

What schools have you attended?_____

THE BLUMENFELD ORAL READING ASSESSMENT TEST

Marking Copy (Version A)

Name			Age	Grade	Date	
1	**2**	**3**	**4**	**5**	**6**	**7**
mad	dad	make	leak	time	joke	tune
yen	vex	paid	yield	like	boat	fuse
bit	dim	wait	she	sight	soap	huge
hog	fog	game	dream	size	row	crude
mum	cub	eight	weep	fire	cold	new
nap	jam	say	seat	cry	nose	blue
let	yet	jail	mean	dice	hope	chew
rib	fig	cage	treat	shy	phone	juice
top	cop	weigh	seed	high	slow	zoo
dug	gut	fade	brief	price	dome	spoon
8	**9**	**10**	**11**	**12**	**13**	**14**
food	out	Joyce	car	ball	serve	fam
wood	now	toy	sharp	yawn	term	hap
should	house	boil	spark	fault	girl	dex
pool	count	coin	charm	raw	shirt	seg
too	brown	void	chart	cause	thirst	dib
room	ounce	boy	charge	talk	nurse	min
book	ground	moist	farce	haunt	earn	jod
could	crowd	Troy	card	crawl	earth	nov
crook	owl	foil	large	call	worm	lub
nook	our	join	arch	caught	burn	sut

NOTE: Teacher may wish to remove for ease of scoring

THE BLUMENFELD ORAL READING ASSESSMENT TEST

15	16	17	18	19	20
blunt	slump	trust	able	who	this
brash	shrimp	thrash	fiddle	eye	which
clamp	smash	twitch	cattle	your	chap
crutch	snarl	preach	struggle	where	sheath
dredge	sprang	threat	single	young	while
dwell	stomp	streak	fumble	pull	church
flush	strand	text	stifle	door	rash
frost	swift	kept	wriggle	enough	those
grudge	scalp	brisk	strangle	sew	when
prompt	scrunch	draft	turtle	touch	ash

21	22	23	24	25	26
nation	scheme	Philip	napkin	promptly	national
action	chorus	phony	gallon	begrudge	consumption
patient	chemist	phrase	chapel	slothful	imagine
mission	school	physics	kidnap	tactless	tyranny
special	Christmas	graphic	vivid	luncheon	possible
capture	psychic	photo	pencil	witchcraft	difference
question	myth	rough	mimic	chopstick	judicious
fusion	system	cough	vanish	swiftly	represent
leisure	syntax	laugh	cactus	cascade	incident
tissue	syrup	draught	signal	spaceship	consonant

THE BLUMENFELD ORAL READING ASSESSMENT TEST

27	28	29	30	31
concern	chastened	artisan	eccentric	manager
routine	contrite	subsidies	applicants	information
asphalt	realty	upheavals	excesses	registration
prepare	apprised	ascertain	epithets	biographical
nasal	derived	resilience	exultant	photogenic
assigned	pattern	prodigious	contrary	discovery
rely	inane	equity	imminent	immediately
triumph	regime	potentate	fortified	supervision
bestow	novice	lunacy	conveyor	vacation
technique	precepts	antidote	decisive	environment

32	33	34	35
interrogation	diminutive	irresponsible	indignation
concentrated	spontaneous	surreptitiously	undemocratically
inconceivable	tremendously	representative	customarily
collaboration	emulation	consanguinity	idiosyncracies
accomplices	apostrophe	justifiable	indistinguishable
deregulation	revolution	totalitarian	intimidated
reapportionment	enunciate	infallibility	entrepreneur
contemptuous	conscientious	analytical	simultaneously
incompatibility	dictatorship	climatology	interminable
formidable	combustible	anonymity	meticulously

THE BLUMENFELD ORAL READING ASSESSMENT TEST

36	37	38
illumination	candidate	microprocessor
unimaginable	productivity	facilities
replicated	exceptional	confidential
reverberating	pneumatic	multidisciplinary
ludicrously	semiconductor	neurosurgery
computerized	collateral	coordinator
contiguous	appropriate	prototypes
ephemeral	responsibilities	negotiations
resuscitated	manufacturing	synonymous
anesthesiologist	innovation	installation

Score (Number of errors by column)

1___	11___	21___	31___
2___	12___	22___	32___
3___	13___	23___	33___
4___	14___	24___	34___
5___	15___	25___	35___
6___	16___	26___	36___
7___	17___	27___	37___
8___	18___	28___	38___
9___	19___	29___	
10___	20___	30___	Total___

Final Score_____ Reading Grade Level _____

Do you plan to attend a college? _____

What is your career goal?_____

What schools have you attended?_____

THE BLUMENFELD ORAL READING ASSESSMENT TEST

Marking Copy (Version A)

Name				Age	Grade	Date

1	2	3	4	5	6	7
mad	dad	make	leak	time	joke	tune
yen	vex	paid	yield	like	boat	fuse
bit	dim	wait	she	sight	soap	huge
hog	fog	game	dream	size	row	crude
mum	cub	eight	weep	fire	cold	new
nap	jam	say	seat	cry	nose	blue
let	yet	jail	mean	dice	hope	chew
rib	fig	cage	treat	shy	phone	juice
top	cop	weigh	seed	high	slow	zoo
dug	gut	fade	brief	price	dome	spoon

NOTE: Teacher may wish to remove for ease of scoring

8	9	10	11	12	13	14
food	out	Joyce	car	ball	serve	fam
wood	now	toy	sharp	yawn	term	hap
should	house	boil	spark	fault	girl	dex
pool	count	coin	charm	raw	shirt	seg
too	brown	void	chart	cause	thirst	dib
room	ounce	boy	charge	talk	nurse	min
book	ground	moist	farce	haunt	earn	jod
could	crowd	Troy	card	crawl	earth	nov
crook	owl	foil	large	call	worm	lub
nook	our	join	arch	caught	burn	sut

THE BLUMENFELD ORAL READING ASSESSMENT TEST

15	16	17	18	19	20
blunt	slump	trust	able	who	this
brash	shrimp	thrash	fiddle	eye	which
clamp	smash	twitch	cattle	your	chap
crutch	snarl	preach	struggle	where	sheath
dredge	sprang	threat	single	young	while
dwell	stomp	streak	fumble	pull	church
flush	strand	text	stifle	door	rash
frost	swift	kept	wriggle	enough	those
grudge	scalp	brisk	strangle	sew	when
prompt	scrunch	draft	turtle	touch	ash

21	22	23	24	25	26
nation	scheme	Philip	napkin	promptly	national
action	chorus	phony	gallon	begrudge	consumption
patient	chemist	phrase	chapel	slothful	imagine
mission	school	physics	kidnap	tactless	tyranny
special	Christmas	graphic	vivid	luncheon	possible
capture	psychic	photo	pencil	witchcraft	difference
question	myth	rough	mimic	chopstick	judicious
fusion	system	cough	vanish	swiftly	represent
leisure	syntax	laugh	cactus	cascade	incident
tissue	syrup	draught	signal	spaceship	consonant

THE BLUMENFELD ORAL READING ASSESSMENT TEST

27	28	29	30	31
concern	chastened	artisan	eccentric	manager
routine	contrite	subsidies	applicants	information
asphalt	realty	upheavals	excesses	registration
prepare	apprised	ascertain	epithets	biographical
nasal	derived	resilience	exultant	photogenic
assigned	pattern	prodigious	contrary	discovery
rely	inane	equity	imminent	immediately
triumph	regime	potentate	fortified	supervision
bestow	novice	lunacy	conveyor	vacation
technique	precepts	antidote	decisive	environment

32	33	34	35
interrogation	diminutive	irresponsible	indignation
concentrated	spontaneous	surreptitiously	undemocratically
inconceivable	tremendously	representative	customarily
collaboration	emulation	consanguinity	idiosyncracies
accomplices	apostrophe	justifiable	indistinguishable
deregulation	revolution	totalitarian	intimidated
reapportionment	enunciate	infallibility	entrepreneur
contemptuous	conscientious	analytical	simultaneously
incompatibility	dictatorship	climatology	interminable
formidable	combustible	anonymity	meticulously

THE BLUMENFELD ORAL READING ASSESSMENT TEST

36	37	38
illumination	candidate	microprocessor
unimaginable	productivity	facilities
replicated	exceptional	confidential
reverberating	pneumatic	multidisciplinary
ludicrously	semiconductor	neurosurgery
computerized	collateral	coordinator
contiguous	appropriate	prototypes
ephemeral	responsibilities	negotiations
resuscitated	manufacturing	synonymous
anesthesiologist	innovation	installation

Score (Number of errors by column)

1___	11___	21___	31___
2___	12___	22___	32___
3___	13___	23___	33___
4___	14___	24___	34___
5___	15___	25___	35___
6___	16___	26___	36___
7___	17___	27___	37___
8___	18___	28___	38___
9___	19___	29___	
10___	20___	30___	Total___

Final Score_____ Reading Grade Level _____

Do you plan to attend a college? _____

What is your career goal?_____

What schools have you attended?_____

The Blumenfeld Oral Reading Assessment Test
Marking Copy (Version B)

Name _____   Age _____   Grade _____   Date _____

1	2	3	4	5	6	7
fad	dab	bake	peak	dime	poke	dune
yet	wax	maid	shield	bike	coat	muse
lit	did	gait	we	light	soar	huge
bog	gut	tame	cream	prize	crow	rude
sum	cup	weight	seep	hire	fold	few
pan	jet	day	bleat	fry	pose	true
met	yam	fail	clean	nice	rope	shrew
dim	fog	page	feat	sty	moan	sluice
hop	cob	vein	deed	thigh	grow	goof
mug	gut	wade	chief	thrice	home	croon

NOTE: Teacher may wish to remove for ease of scoring

8	9	10	11	12	13	14
mood	pout	Royce	far	call	nerve	maf
hood	how	coy	harp	dawn	germ	hab
would	douse	foil	stark	fault	girl	yex
cool	mount	loin	shard	clause	burst	beb
shook	crown	voice	carp	jaw	flirt	teg
broom	bounce	joy	charge	balk	purse	hin
cook	found	foist	farce	daunt	learn	jub
could	crowd	ploy	lard	crawl	earth	niv
zoom	fowl	coil	barge	fall	worth	lut
hook	hour	toy	arch	fraught	turn	suz

The Blumenfeld Oral Reading Assessment Test
(Version B)

15	16	17	18	19	20
blast	slump	thrust	fable	whom	thin
brush	swamp	brash	riddle	eye	which
clump	stash	twitch	bottle	your	champ
crash	snarl	breach	straggle	were	shield
drudge	spring	sweat	mingle	youngster	whilst
dwarf	stump	strength	stumble	bull	church
flash	string	next	trifle	floors	dash
front	shrift	crept	wriggle	enough	these
graft	scalp	brusk	wrangle	two	what
prompt	scrounge	craft	hurtle	only	fresh

21	22	23	24	25	26
station	schedule	Phyllis	tidbit	spendthrift	sensation
faction	choral	phone	ribbon	slingshot	assumption
patience	chemical	phase	tablet	crankcase	imagine
fission	scholar	physical	picnic	dustpan	despotic
racial	Christian	graphite	civil	flagpoles	probable
rapture	psychotic	phosphate	within	crispness	diffident
bastion	mythical	tough	liquid	grandstand	dominion
pleasure	symphony	cough	blemish	spotless	resentment
lesion	systemic	laughter	mascot	hamstring	commodity
issue	character	draught	lentil	platelet	accident

The Blumenfeld Oral Reading Assessment Test
(Version B)

27	28	29	30	31
preserve	hastened	partisan	nemesis	principal
berserk	epoch	rapsodies	reprisal	semester
censure	fledgling	magnesia	skeptical	scholastic
asthma	grenade	novella	hypoderm	historical
diffuse	deprived	reprobate	gardenia	vaccinations
resigned	inscribe	hydrofoil	aqueduct	autobiographical
defy	demure	demagogue	asterisk	counselor
chromic	maestro	permeate	eminent	supervisory
betroth	limelight	placebo	bivouac	ecological
physique	mortgage	thoroughfare	coercive	valedictorian

32	33	34	35
interrogatory	femininity	unalienable	pathogenesis
concentration	gentility	reconnaissance	confiscatory
coincidental	guarantee	septuagenarian	stereotypical
dialectic	heterogeneous	stratagem	idiosyncratic
appropriate	ideogram	hierarchy	premeditated
asinine	inscrutable	espionage	pseudonym
craniology	modification	inviolability	rigmarole
denationalize	obsolescence	ludicrous	knavery
epileptic	pistachio	noncarnivorous	hypocritically
facetious	polytheism	obstetrician	quiescent

The Blumenfeld Oral Reading Assessment Test
(Version B)

36	37	38
hypochondriac	sophistication	radioactivity
impermeable	ministerial	simulator
diversionary	elegiac	privatization
matriculate	gregarious	statistician
mercenary	pneumonia	tautology
onomatopoeia	lobotomy	ventriloquy
lithography	immunology	topographer
perfunctory	libertarianism	mistletoe
quintessential	rejuvenation	individualize
schizophrenic	malfeasance	extraterrestrial

Score (Number of errors by column)

1 ___	11 ___	21 ___	31 ___
2 ___	12 ___	22 ___	32 ___
3 ___	13 ___	23 ___	33 ___
4 ___	14 ___	24 ___	34 ___
5 ___	15 ___	25 ___	35 ___
6 ___	16 ___	26 ___	36 ___
7 ___	17 ___	27 ___	37 ___
8 ___	18 ___	28 ___	38 ___
9 ___	19 ___	29 ___	
10 ___	20 ___	30 ___	Total ___

Score (Test version A) _____ Score (Test version B)_____

Date of above test _____ Date of above test _____

The Blumenfeld Oral Reading Assessment Test
Marking Copy (Version B)

Name _____ Age _____ Grade _____ Date _____

1	2	3	4	5	6	7
fad	dab	bake	peak	dime	poké	dune
yet	wax	maid	shield	bike	coat	muse
lit	did	gait	we	light	soar	huge
bog	gut	tame	cream	prize	crow	rude
sum	cup	weight	seep	hire	fold	few
pan	jet	day	bleat	fry	pose	true
met	yam	fail	clean	nice	rope	shrew
dim	fog	page	feat	sty	moan	sluice
hop	cob	vein	deed	thigh	grow	goof
mug	gut	wade	chief	thrice	home	croon

8	9	10	11	12	13	14
mood	pout	Royce	far	call	nerve	maf
hood	how	coy	harp	dawn	germ	hab
would	douse	foil	stark	fault	girl	yex
cool	mount	loin	shard	clause	burst	beb
shook	crown	voice	carp	jaw	flirt	teg
broom	bounce	joy	charge	balk	purse	hin
cook	found	foist	farce	daunt	learn	jub
could	crowd	ploy	lard	crawl	earth	niv
zoom	fowl	coil	barge	fall	worth	lut
hook	hour	toy	arch	fraught	turn	suz

NOTE: Teacher may wish to remove for ease of scoring

The Blumenfeld Oral Reading Assessment Test
(Version B)

15	16	17	18	19	20
blast	slump	thrust	fable	whom	thin
brush	swamp	brash	riddle	eye	which
clump	stash	twitch	bottle	your	champ
crash	snarl	breach	straggle	were	shield
drudge	spring	sweat	mingle	youngster	whilst
dwarf	stump	strength	stumble	bull	church
flash	string	next	trifle	floors	dash
front	shrift	crept	wriggle	enough	these
graft	scalp	brusk	wrangle	two	what
prompt	scrounge	craft	hurtle	only	fresh

21	22	23	24	25	26
station	schedule	Phyllis	tidbit	spendthrift	sensation
faction	choral	phone	ribbon	slingshot	assumption
patience	chemical	phase	tablet	crankcase	imagine
fission	scholar	physical	picnic	dustpan	despotic
racial	Christian	graphite	civil	flagpoles	probable
rapture	psychotic	phosphate	within	crispness	diffident
bastion	mythical	tough	liquid	grandstand	dominion
pleasure	symphony	cough	blemish	spotless	resentment
lesion	systemic	laughter	mascot	hamstring	commodity
issue	character	draught	lentil	platelet	accident

The Blumenfeld Oral Reading Assessment Test
(Version B)

27	28	29	30	31
preserve	hastened	partisan	nemesis	principal
berserk	epoch	rapsodies	reprisal	semester
censure	fledgling	magnesia	skeptical	scholastic
asthma	grenade	novella	hypoderm	historical
diffuse	deprived	reprobate	gardenia	vaccinations
resigned	inscribe	hydrofoil	aqueduct	autobiographical
defy	demure	demagogue	asterisk	counselor
chromic	maestro	permeate	eminent	supervisory
betroth	limelight	placebo	bivouac	ecological
physique	mortgage	thoroughfare	coercive	valedictorian

32	33	34	35
interrogatory	femininity	unalienable	pathogenesis
concentration	gentility	reconnaissance	confiscatory
coincidental	guarantee	septuagenarian	stereotypical
dialectic	heterogeneous	stratagem	idiosyncratic
appropriate	ideogram	hierarchy	premeditated
asinine	inscrutable	espionage	pseudonym
craniology	modification	inviolability	rigmarole
denationalize	obsolescence	ludicrous	knavery
epileptic	pistachio	noncarnivorous	hypocritically
facetious	polytheism	obstetrician	quiescent

The Blumenfeld Oral Reading Assessment Test
(Version B)

36	37	38
hypochondriac	sophistication	radioactivity
impermeable	ministerial	simulator
diversionary	elegiac	privatization
matriculate	gregarious	statistician
mercenary	pneumonia	tautology
onomatopoeia	lobotomy	ventriloquy
lithography	immunology	topographer
perfunctory	libertarianism	mistletoe
quintessential	rejuvenation	individualize
schizophrenic	malfeasance	extraterrestrial

Score (Number of errors by column)

1___	11___	21___	31___
2___	12___	22___	32___
3___	13___	23___	33___
4___	14___	24___	34___
5___	15___	25___	35___
6___	16___	26___	36___
7___	17___	27___	37___
8___	18___	28___	38___
9___	19___	29___	
10___	20___	30___	Total___

Score (Test version A) _____ Score (Test version B)_____

Date of above test _____Date of above test _____

The Blumenfeld Oral Reading Assessment Test

Marking Copy (Version B)

Name _____ Age _____ Grade _____ Date _____

1	2	3	4	5	6	7
fad	dab	bake	peak	dime	poke	dune
yet	wax	maid	shield	bike	coat	muse
lit	did	gait	we	light	soar	huge
bog	gut	tame	cream	prize	crow	rude
sum	cup	weight	seep	hire	fold	few
pan	jet	day	bleat	fry	pose	true
met	yam	fail	clean	nice	rope	shrew
dim	fog	page	feat	sty	moan	sluice
hop	cob	vein	deed	thigh	grow	goof
mug	gut	wade	chief	thrice	home	croon

8	9	10	11	12	13	14
mood	pout	Royce	far	call	nerve	maf
hood	how	coy	harp	dawn	germ	hab
would	douse	foil	stark	fault	girl	yex
cool	mount	loin	shard	clause	burst	beb
shook	crown	voice	carp	jaw	flirt	teg
broom	bounce	joy	charge	balk	purse	hin
cook	found	foist	farce	daunt	learn	jub
could	crowd	ploy	lard	crawl	earth	niv
zoom	fowl	coil	barge	fall	worth	lut
hook	hour	toy	arch	fraught	turn	suz

NOTE: Teacher may wish to remove for ease of scoring

The Blumenfeld Oral Reading Assessment Test
(Version B)

15	16	17	18	19	20
blast	slump	thrust	fable	whom	thin
brush	swamp	brash	riddle	eye	which
clump	stash	twitch	bottle	your	champ
crash	snarl	breach	straggle	were	shield
drudge	spring	sweat	mingle	youngster	whilst
dwarf	stump	strength	stumble	bull	church
flash	string	next	trifle	floors	dash
front	shrift	crept	wriggle	enough	these
graft	scalp	brusk	wrangle	two	what
prompt	scrounge	craft	hurtle	only	fresh

21	22	23	24	25	26
station	schedule	Phyllis	tidbit	spendthrift	sensation
faction	choral	phone	ribbon	slingshot	assumption
patience	chemical	phase	tablet	crankcase	imagine
fission	scholar	physical	picnic	dustpan	despotic
racial	Christian	graphite	civil	flagpoles	probable
rapture	psychotic	phosphate	within	crispness	diffident
bastion	mythical	tough	liquid	grandstand	dominion
pleasure	symphony	cough	blemish	spotless	resentment
lesion	systemic	laughter	mascot	hamstring	commodity
issue	character	draught	lentil	platelet	accident

The Blumenfeld Oral Reading Assessment Test
(Version B)

27	28	29	30	31
preserve	hastened	partisan	nemesis	principal
berserk	epoch	rapsodies	reprisal	semester
censure	fledgling	magnesia	skeptical	scholastic
asthma	grenade	novella	hypoderm	historical
diffuse	deprived	reprobate	gardenia	vaccinations
resigned	inscribe	hydrofoil	aqueduct	autobiographical
defy	demure	demagogue	asterisk	counselor
chromic	maestro	permeate	eminent	supervisory
betroth	limelight	placebo	bivouac	ecological
physique	mortgage	thoroughfare	coercive	valedictorian

32	33	34	35
interrogatory	femininity	unalienable	pathogenesis
concentration	gentility	reconnaissance	confiscatory
coincidental	guarantee	septuagenarian	stereotypical
dialectic	heterogeneous	stratagem	idiosyncratic
appropriate	ideogram	hierarchy	premeditated
asinine	inscrutable	espionage	pseudonym
craniology	modification	inviolability	rigmarole
denationalize	obsolescence	ludicrous	knavery
epileptic	pistachio	noncarnivorous	hypocritically
facetious	polytheism	obstetrician	quiescent

The Blumenfeld Oral Reading Assessment Test
(Version B)

36	37	38
hypochondriac	sophistication	radioactivity
impermeable	ministerial	simulator
diversionary	elegiac	privatization
matriculate	gregarious	statistician
mercenary	pneumonia	tautology
onomatopoeia	lobotomy	ventriloquy
lithography	immunology	topographer
perfunctory	libertarianism	mistletoe
quintessential	rejuvenation	individualize
schizophrenic	malfeasance	extraterrestrial

Score (Number of errors by column)

1___	11___	21___	31___
2___	12___	22___	32___
3___	13___	23___	33___
4___	14___	24___	34___
5___	15___	25___	35___
6___	16___	26___	36___
7___	17___	27___	37___
8___	18___	28___	38___
9___	19___	29___	
10___	20___	30___	Total___

Score (Test version A) _____ Score (Test version B)_____

Date of above test _____ Date of above test _____

The Blumenfeld Oral Reading Assessment Test
Marking Copy (Version B)

Name _____ Age _____ Grade _____ Date _____

1	2	3	4	5	6	7
fad	dab	bake	peak	dime	poke	dune
yet	wax	maid	shield	bike	coat	muse
lit	did	gait	we	light	soar	huge
bog	gut	tame	cream	prize	crow	rude
sum	cup	weight	seep	hire	fold	few
pan	jet	day	bleat	fry	pose	true
met	yam	fail	clean	nice	rope	shrew
dim	fog	page	feat	sty	moan	sluice
hop	cob	vein	deed	thigh	grow	goof
mug	gut	wade	chief	thrice	home	croon

8	9	10	11	12	13	14
mood	pout	Royce	far	call	nerve	maf
hood	how	coy	harp	dawn	germ	hab
would	douse	foil	stark	fault	girl	yex
cool	mount	loin	shard	clause	burst	beb
shook	crown	voice	carp	jaw	flirt	teg
broom	bounce	joy	charge	balk	purse	hin
cook	found	foist	farce	daunt	learn	jub
could	crowd	ploy	lard	crawl	earth	niv
zoom	fowl	coil	barge	fall	worth	lut
hook	hour	toy	arch	fraught	turn	suz

NOTE: Teacher may wish to remove for ease of scoring

The Blumenfeld Oral Reading Assessment Test
(Version B)

15	16	17	18	19	20
blast	slump	thrust	fable	whom	thin
brush	swamp	brash	riddle	eye	which
clump	stash	twitch	bottle	your	champ
crash	snarl	breach	straggle	were	shield
drudge	spring	sweat	mingle	youngster	whilst
dwarf	stump	strength	stumble	bull	church
flash	string	next	trifle	floors	dash
front	shrift	crept	wriggle	enough	these
graft	scalp	brusk	wrangle	two	what
prompt	scrounge	craft	hurtle	only	fresh

21	22	23	24	25	26
station	schedule	Phyllis	tidbit	spendthrift	sensation
faction	choral	phone	ribbon	slingshot	assumption
patience	chemical	phase	tablet	crankcase	imagine
fission	scholar	physical	picnic	dustpan	despotic
racial	Christian	graphite	civil	flagpoles	probable
rapture	psychotic	phosphate	within	crispness	diffident
bastion	mythical	tough	liquid	grandstand	dominion
pleasure	symphony	cough	blemish	spotless	resentment
lesion	systemic	laughter	mascot	hamstring	commodity
issue	character	draught	lentil	platelet	accident

The Blumenfeld Oral Reading Assessment Test
(Version B)

27	28	29	30	31
preserve	hastened	partisan	nemesis	principal
berserk	epoch	rapsodies	reprisal	semester
censure	fledgling	magnesia	skeptical	scholastic
asthma	grenade	novella	hypoderm	historical
diffuse	deprived	reprobate	gardenia	vaccinations
resigned	inscribe	hydrofoil	aqueduct	autobiographical
defy	demure	demagogue	asterisk	counselor
chromic	maestro	permeate	eminent	supervisory
betroth	limelight	placebo	bivouac	ecological
physique	mortgage	thoroughfare	coercive	valedictorian

32	33	34	35
interrogatory	femininity	unalienable	pathogenesis
concentration	gentility	reconnaissance	confiscatory
coincidental	guarantee	septuagenarian	stereotypical
dialectic	heterogeneous	stratagem	idiosyncratic
appropriate	ideogram	hierarchy	premeditated
asinine	inscrutable	espionage	pseudonym
craniology	modification	inviolability	rigmarole
denationalize	obsolescence	ludicrous	knavery
epileptic	pistachio	noncarnivorous	hypocritically
facetious	polytheism	obstetrician	quiescent

The Blumenfeld Oral Reading Assessment Test
(Version B)

36	37	38
hypochondriac	sophistication	radioactivity
impermeable	ministerial	simulator
diversionary	elegiac	privatization
matriculate	gregarious	statistician
mercenary	pneumonia	tautology
onomatopoeia	lobotomy	ventriloquy
lithography	immunology	topographer
perfunctory	libertarianism	mistletoe
quintessential	rejuvenation	individualize
schizophrenic	malfeasance	extraterrestrial

Score (Number of errors by column)

1___	11___	21___	31___
2___	12___	22___	32___
3___	13___	23___	33___
4___	14___	24___	34___
5___	15___	25___	35___
6___	16___	26___	36___
7___	17___	27___	37___
8___	18___	28___	38___
9___	19___	29___	
10___	20___	30___	Total___

Score (Test version A) _____ Score (Test version B)_____

Date of above test _____ Date of above test _____

The Blumenfeld Oral Reading Assessment Test
Marking Copy (Version B)

Name   Age   Grade   Date

1	2	3	4	5	6	7
fad	dab	bake	peak	dime	poke	dune
yet	wax	maid	shield	bike	coat	muse
lit	did	gait	we	light	soar	huge
bog	gut	tame	cream	prize	crow	rude
sum	cup	weight	seep	hire	fold	few
pan	jet	day	bleat	fry	pose	true
met	yam	fail	clean	nice	rope	shrew
dim	fog	page	feat	sty	moan	sluice
hop	cob	vein	deed	thigh	grow	goof
mug	gut	wade	chief	thrice	home	croon

8	9	10	11	12	13	14
mood	pout	Royce	far	call	nerve	maf
hood	how	coy	harp	dawn	germ	hab
would	douse	foil	stark	fault	girl	yex
cool	mount	loin	shard	clause	burst	beb
shook	crown	voice	carp	jaw	flirt	teg
broom	bounce	joy	charge	balk	purse	hin
cook	found	foist	farce	daunt	learn	jub
could	crowd	ploy	lard	crawl	earth	niv
zoom	fowl	coil	barge	fall	worth	lut
hook	hour	toy	arch	fraught	turn	suz

NOTE: Teacher may wish to remove for ease of scoring

The Blumenfeld Oral Reading Assessment Test
(Version B)

15	16	17	18	19	20
blast	slump	thrust	fable	whom	thin
brush	swamp	brash	riddle	eye	which
clump	stash	twitch	bottle	your	champ
crash	snarl	breach	straggle	were	shield
drudge	spring	sweat	mingle	youngster	whilst
dwarf	stump	strength	stumble	bull	church
flash	string	next	trifle	floors	dash
front	shrift	crept	wriggle	enough	these
graft	scalp	brusk	wrangle	two	what
prompt	scrounge	craft	hurtle	only	fresh

21	22	23	24	25	26
station	schedule	Phyllis	tidbit	spendthrift	sensation
faction	choral	phone	ribbon	slingshot	assumption
patience	chemical	phase	tablet	crankcase	imagine
fission	scholar	physical	picnic	dustpan	despotic
racial	Christian	graphite	civil	flagpoles	probable
rapture	psychotic	phosphate	within	crispness	diffident
bastion	mythical	tough	liquid	grandstand	dominion
pleasure	symphony	cough	blemish	spotless	resentment
lesion	systemic	laughter	mascot	hamstring	commodity
issue	character	draught	lentil	platelet	accident

The Blumenfeld Oral Reading Assessment Test
(Version B)

27	28	29	30	31
preserve	hastened	partisan	nemesis	principal
berserk	epoch	rapsodies	reprisal	semester
censure	fledgling	magnesia	skeptical	scholastic
asthma	grenade	novella	hypoderm	historical
diffuse	deprived	reprobate	gardenia	vaccinations
resigned	inscribe	hydrofoil	aqueduct	autobiographical
defy	demure	demagogue	asterisk	counselor
chromic	maestro	permeate	eminent	supervisory
betroth	limelight	placebo	bivouac	ecological
physique	mortgage	thoroughfare	coercive	valedictorian

32	33	34	35
interrogatory	femininity	unalienable	pathogenesis
concentration	gentility	reconnaissance	confiscatory
coincidental	guarantee	septuagenarian	stereotypical
dialectic	heterogeneous	stratagem	idiosyncratic
appropriate	ideogram	hierarchy	premeditated
asinine	inscrutable	espionage	pseudonym
craniology	modification	inviolability	rigmarole
denationalize	obsolescence	ludicrous	knavery
epileptic	pistachio	noncarnivorous	hypocritically
facetious	polytheism	obstetrician	quiescent

The Blumenfeld Oral Reading Assessment Test
(Version B)

36	37	38
hypochondriac	sophistication	radioactivity
impermeable	ministerial	simulator
diversionary	elegiac	privatization
matriculate	gregarious	statistician
mercenary	pneumonia	tautology
onomatopoeia	lobotomy	ventriloquy
lithography	immunology	topographer
perfunctory	libertarianism	mistletoe
quintessential	rejuvenation	individualize
schizophrenic	malfeasance	extraterrestrial

Score (Number of errors by column)

1___	11___	21___	31___
2___	12___	22___	32___
3___	13___	23___	33___
4___	14___	24___	34___
5___	15___	25___	35___
6___	16___	26___	36___
7___	17___	27___	37___
8___	18___	28___	38___
9___	19___	29___	
10___	20___	30___	Total___

Score (Test version A) _____ Score (Test version B)_____

Date of above test _____Date of above test _____